Other titles in the series:
The Crazy World of Cats (Bill Stott)
The Crazy World of Cricket (Bill Stott)
The Crazy World of Gardening (Bill Stott)
The Crazy World of Golf (Mike Scott)
The Crazy World of the Handyman (Roland Fiddy)
The Crazy World of Hospitals (Bill Stott)
The Crazy World of Housework (Bill Stott)
The Crazy World of Marriage (Bill Stott)
The Crazy World of Rugby (Bill Stott)
The Crazy World of Sailing (Peter Rigby)
The Crazy World of Sex (David Pye)

Published simultaneously in 1992 by Exley Publications Ltd. in Great
Britain, and Exley Giftbooks in the USA.

Copyright © Barry Knowles, 1992

ISBN 1-85015-347-7

A copy of the CIP data is available from the
British Library on request.
Printed in Spain by Grafo S.A., Bilbao.

Exley Publications Ltd, 16 Chalk Hill, Watford, Herts WD1 4BN,
United Kingdom.
Exley Giftbooks, 359 East Main Street, Suite 3D, Mount Kisco,
NY 10549, USA.

the CRAZY world of the GREENS

Cartoons by
Barry Knowles

EXLEY

MT. KISCO, NEW YORK • WATFORD, UK

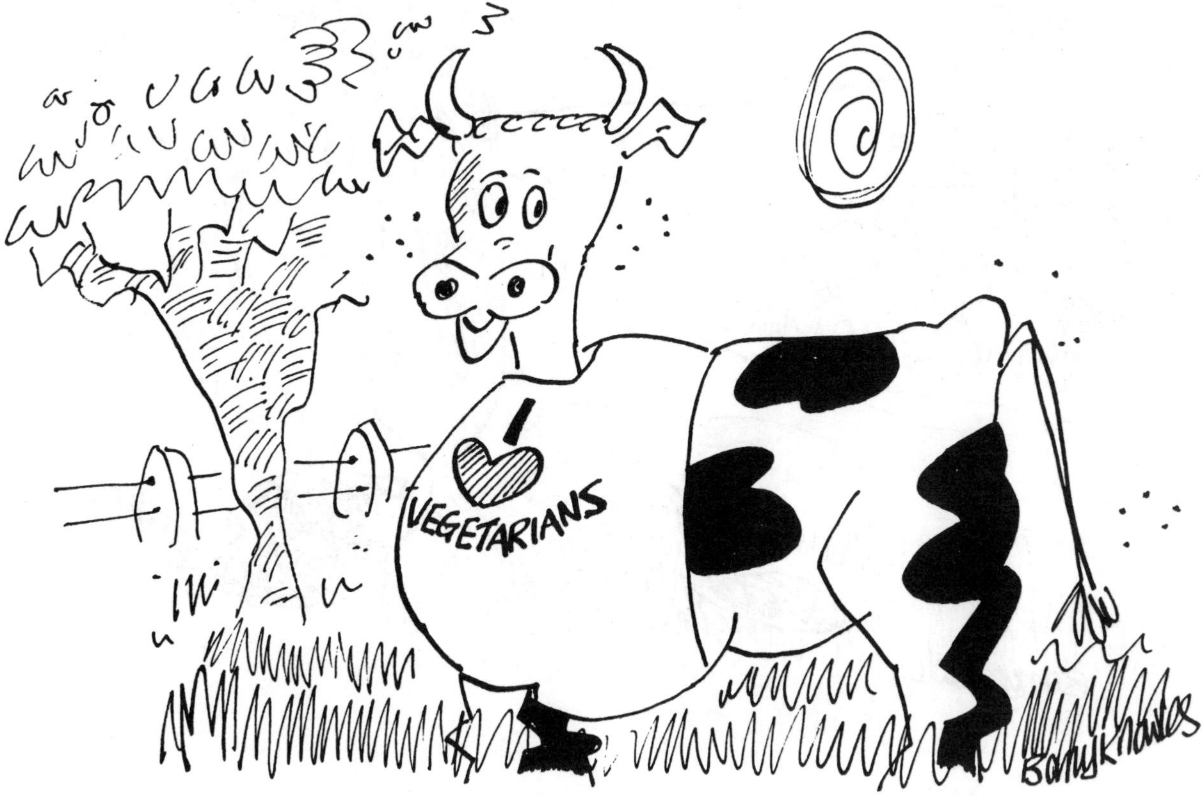
I
VEGETARIANS

"What's it to be – the beavers or the trees ...?"

"Thanks – you saved my life ..."

LEAD-FREE
STAINED GLASS WINDOW

DE-TOX
TENT

FROM HERE YOU CAN SEE FOUR CROP SPRAYINGS

"Is that how the recycling craze started ...?"

"I caught them by creeping up behind and trumpeting loudly ..."

"You can't win, can you?"

"George – what does the word 'sunrise' mean ...?"

"Psst! Filthy junk hamburgers ..."

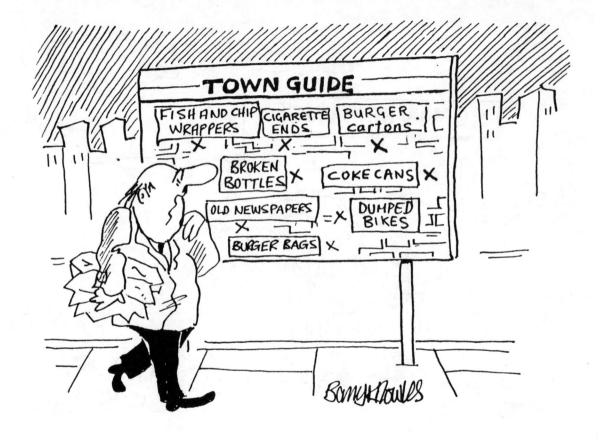

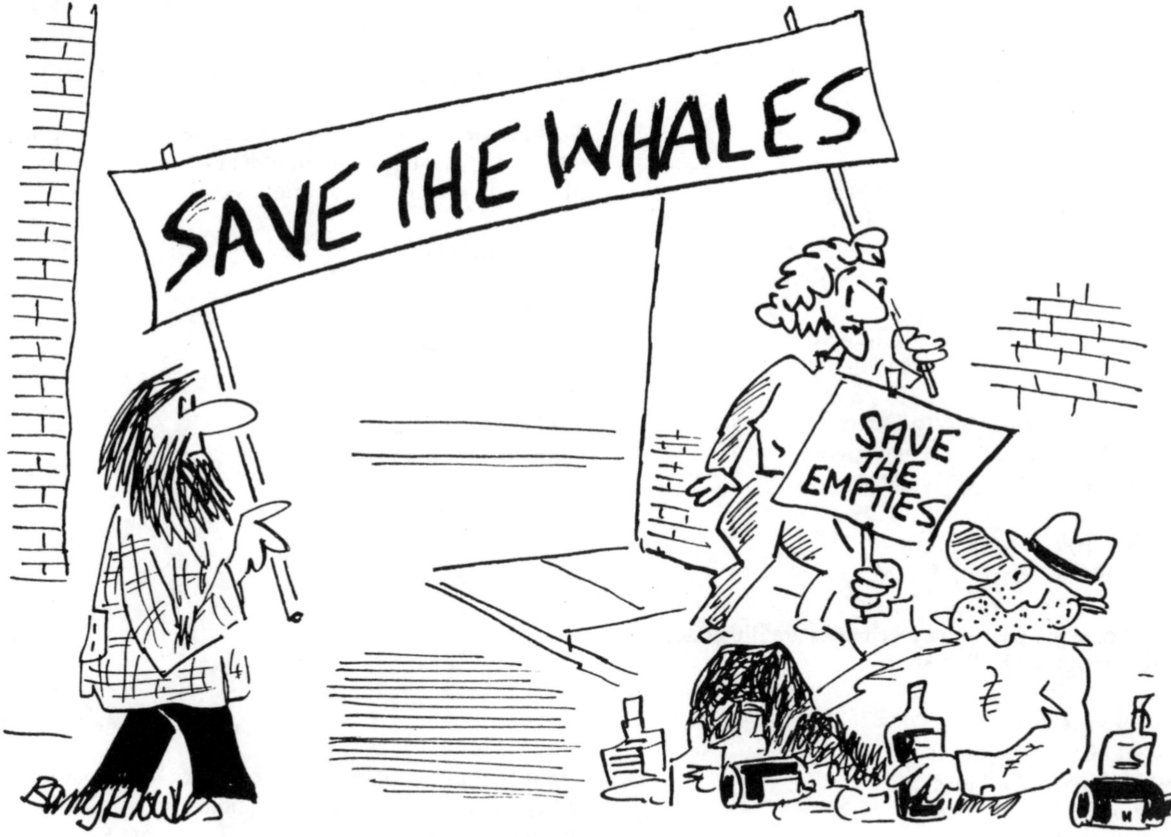
SAVE THE WHALES
SAVE THE EMPTIES

Books in the "Crazy World" series
($4.99 £2.99 paperback)

The Crazy World of Cats (Bill Stott)
The Crazy World of Cricket (Bill Stott)
The Crazy World of Gardening (Bill Stott)
The Crazy World of Golf (Mike Scott)
The Crazy World of the Greens (Barry Knowles)
The Crazy World of the Handyman (Roland Fiddy)
The Crazy World of Hospitals (Bill Stott)
The Crazy World of Housework (Bill Stott)
The Crazy World of Marriage (Bill Stott)
The Crazy World of Rugby (Bill Stott)
The Crazy World of Sailing (Peter Rigby)
The Crazy World of Sex (David Pye)

The Mini Joke Book series
($6.99 £3.99 hardback)

These attractive 64 page mini joke books are illustrated in colour throughout by Bill Stott.

A Binge of Diet Jokes
A Bouquet of Wedding Jokes
A Feast of After Dinner Jokes
A Portfolio of Business Jokes
A Round of Golf Jokes
A Romp of Naughty Jokes
A Spread of Over-40s Jokes

The "Fanatics" series ($4.99 £2.99 paperback)

The **Fanatic's Guides** are perfect presents for everyone with a hobby that has got out of hand. Eighty pages of hilarious black and white cartoons by Roland Fiddy

The Fanatic's Guide to the Bed
The Fanatic's Guide to Cats
The Fanatic's Guide to Computers
The Fanatic's Guide to Dads
The Fanatic's Guide to Diets
The Fanatic's Guide to Dogs
The Fanatic's Guide to Husbands
The Fanatic's Guide to Money
The Fanatic's Guide to Sex
The Fanatic's Guide to Skiing

Great Britain: Order these super books from your local bookseller or from Exley Publications Ltd, 16 Chalk Hill, Watford, Herts WD1 4BN. (Please send £1.25 to cover postage and packing on 1 book, £2.50 on 2 or more books.)